Nostalgia
Collection

A Dog Called BONZO

Introduction by
Mary Cadogan

The Nostalgia Collection: A Dog called Bonzo

ISBN 0 948248 52 1

Published by HAWK BOOKS LIMITED
Suite 309, Canalot Studios, 222 Kensal Road, London W10 5BN.

This edition Copyright © 1990 Hawk Books Ltd.
Bonzo Copyright © 1990 The Estate of George Studdy.

Designed and Edited by Mike Higgs Graphics.

Printed in England.

Such Stuff as Dreams are made of.

Bonzo Sells a Pup.

A selection of 'Bonzo' postcards.

BONZO THE RESILIENT

by

Mary Cadogan

Bonzo, the small, sleepy-looking doggy star of *The Sketch* from the early 1920s, attracted huge audiences which were made up of both adults and children. His image and exploits spilled over from the pages of the magazine into more areas of popular culture than those of any other British animal strip hero. Indeed, if his creator George Ernest Studdy, had not eventually taken steps to slow down his canine character's career, the Bonzo industry might well have begun to rival the multi-faceted one of Disney's Mickey Mouse.

George Studdy was born in Devon in 1878 and his father, an officer in the Argyll and Sutherland Highlanders, hoped that he would follow a military career. However, at the end of his Dulwich College schooldays Studdy was unfit for the army because of the long-lasting effects of a foot injury sustained during his childhood. The boy loved sketching and making models of engines, so his parents thought that he would make a good engineer and arranged an apprenticeship for him. This was short-lived: Studdy then worked for a period with a firm of stockbrokers and began to take evening classes at Heatherley's Art School in London. Always interested in animals, he spent a term at Calderon's Animal School in Kensington to study animal anatomy as well as drawing.

Very soon he was able to sell his pictures to various publishers. A brilliant and vivid all-round illustrator, he first displayed his special talent for depicting animals in Boer War pictures of Royal Artillery actions which, of course, featured horses. His first published drawing of a dog was for a story written by his brother, Hubert.

George Studdy was to contribute illustrations and cartoons to a wide range of comics *(Big Budget, Funny Pips, Jester and Wonder, etc.)*, magazines and papers *(The Graphic, The Humorist, Little Folks, London Magazine, Punch, Windsor Magazine, The Tatler, The Bystander, Illustrated London News, The Field* and, most of all, *The Sketch)*. In the run-up to the First World War, as well as being published in periodicals, his work was used in advertisements and a series of comic science fiction postcards which he designed.

His versatility was further demonstrated from

1915 when, debarred by his foot injury from enlisting, he produced as his contribution to the war effort, a series of animated films (hailed as 'The Best of All War Cartoons').

After the ending of hostilities, Studdy contributed doggy pictures to *The Sketch* on a regular basis. It was, however, some time before what was known as 'the Studdy dog' acquired a permanent shape and a name. He first appeared as 'Bonzo' on 8th November 1922 (the name being dreamed up by *The Sketch's* editor, Bruce Ingram) in an illustration showing him with one eye closed, having just been stung by a wasp.

Bonzo went from strength to strength, appearing regularly in this publication for seven years, his run ending only because Studdy wanted time and opportunity to create other caricatures and drawings. However, Bonzo was not killed off. He continued to thrive in an enormous variety of spin-offs which included games, jigsaws, soft, celluloid and wooden toys, china figures, cups, plates and cruets, soaps, ornaments and ashtrays. In advertisements his appealing image was used to promote razor blades, collar studs, holidays, paint, cigarettes, rat poison, toffees, quilts and cars. He was even featured in a large neon sign at Piccadilly circus.

Studdy's small dog starred in many books for children, including the *Bonzo Annuals* which ran from 1935 to 1952, with a gap during the war years, and in hundreds of attractive full colour postcards. The preciseness of Bonzo's breed was never established, although a celebrated dog breeder once approached the artist about attempting to produce a Bonzo Terrier strain!

George Studdy married Blanche Landrin, a Parisian, in 1912; the couple had one daughter, Vivienne, and Bonzo's tremendous popularity brought affluence to the family, who lived from the early 1920s in some style at Philbeach Gardens, Kensington. Their household was always enriched by dogs, though none of these apparently resembled Bonzo.

Studdy created several other engaging comic animals, including Ooloo, a cat, for *The Humorist* from 1930. During the Second World War he worked as a draughtsman at Portsmouth Naval dockyards. He died of cancer in 1948, but happily Bonzo's career in books, postcards and spin-offs continued for several years afterwards, and Studdy's special dog still has a large number of fans today from all over the world.

An American 'Bonzo' book published in 1929.

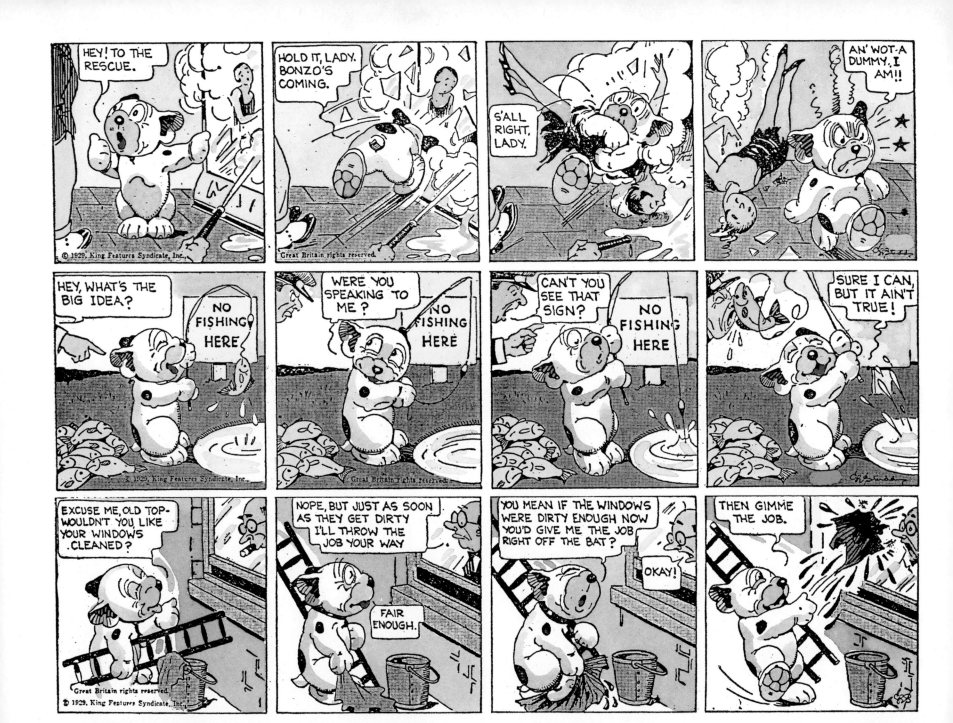

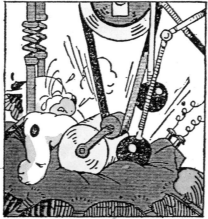

"That's What I Think of You!"

"The Beggars' Opera"

"Out of Luck!"

"Rough Stuff in the Nursery"

His Troubled Dream — When He Snoozed Too Near the Fire.

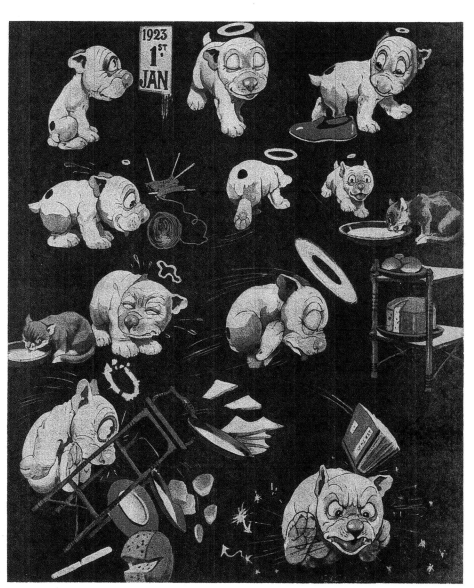

His New Year's Good Resolutions.

Meditations After a Casual Meeting.

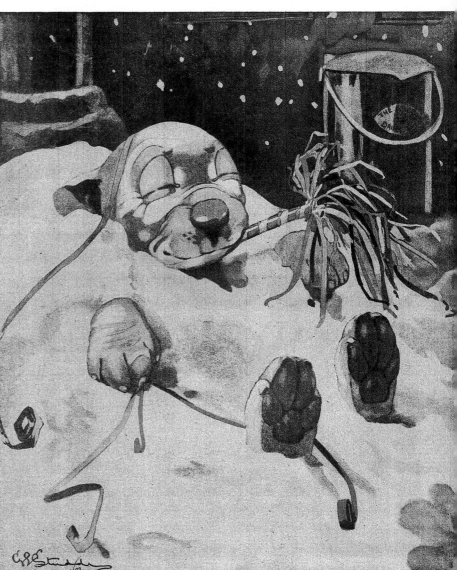

After His Night Out.

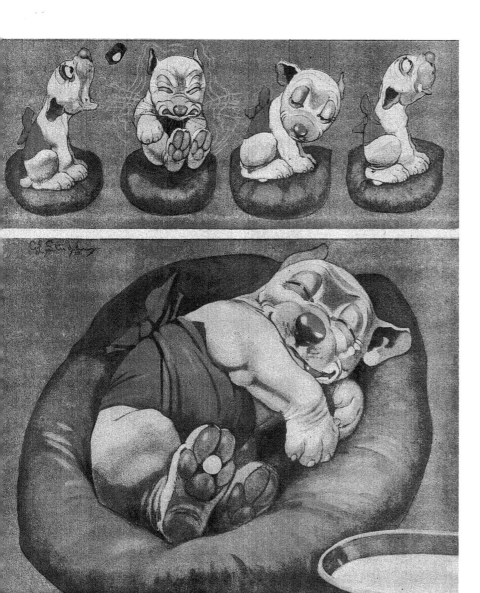

How Bonzo Deceived the Doctor and Palmed the Pill.

Even Bonzo Becomes Interested in the Discoveries in That Egyptian Tomb.

Bonzo's Bath Night.

Bonzo and Chee-Kee Have a Little Mix-Up.

Bonzo Gets That Spring Feeling.

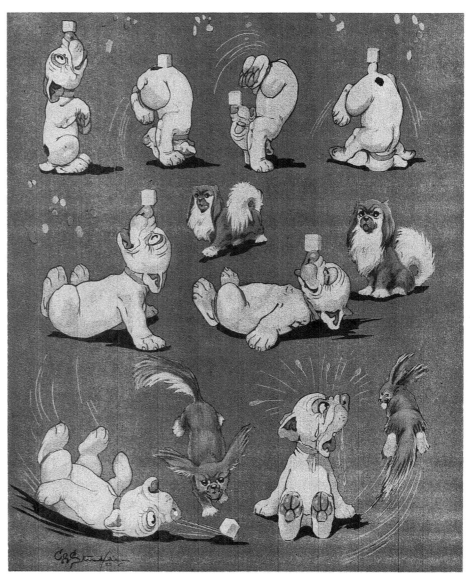

Bonzo Does Parlour Tricks, But Chee-Kee Gets the Reward.

Bonzo Spoils a Perfectly Good Photograph.

Battling Bonzo Wins in the First Round.

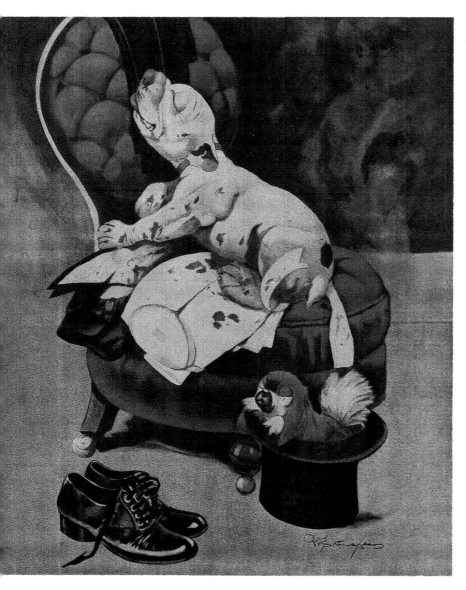

Loyalty!

The Bonzoline Has a Sweet Tooth!

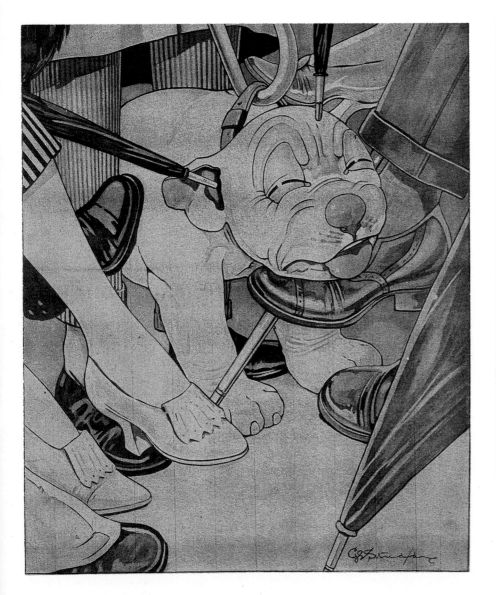

Bonzo Wants His Fare Back!

Hospitality! — Bonzo Is the Victim of a Visitor.

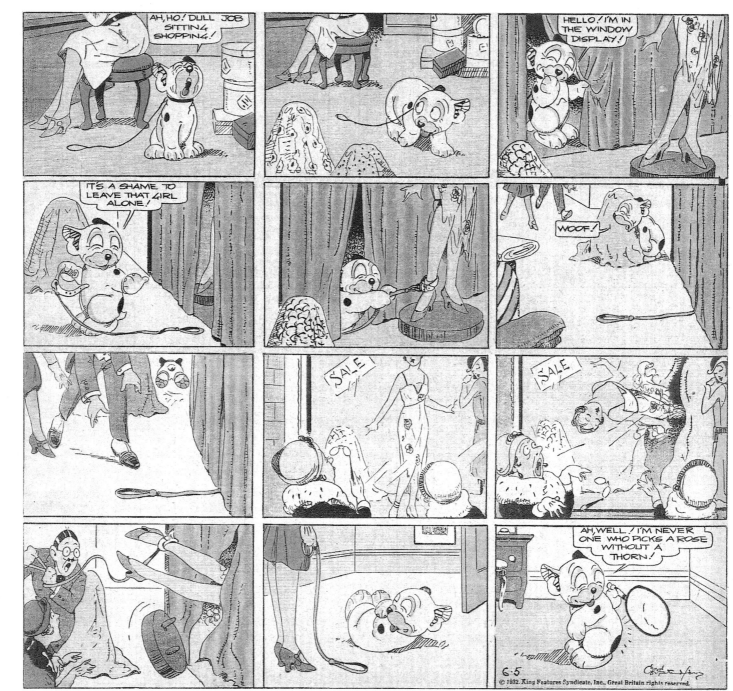

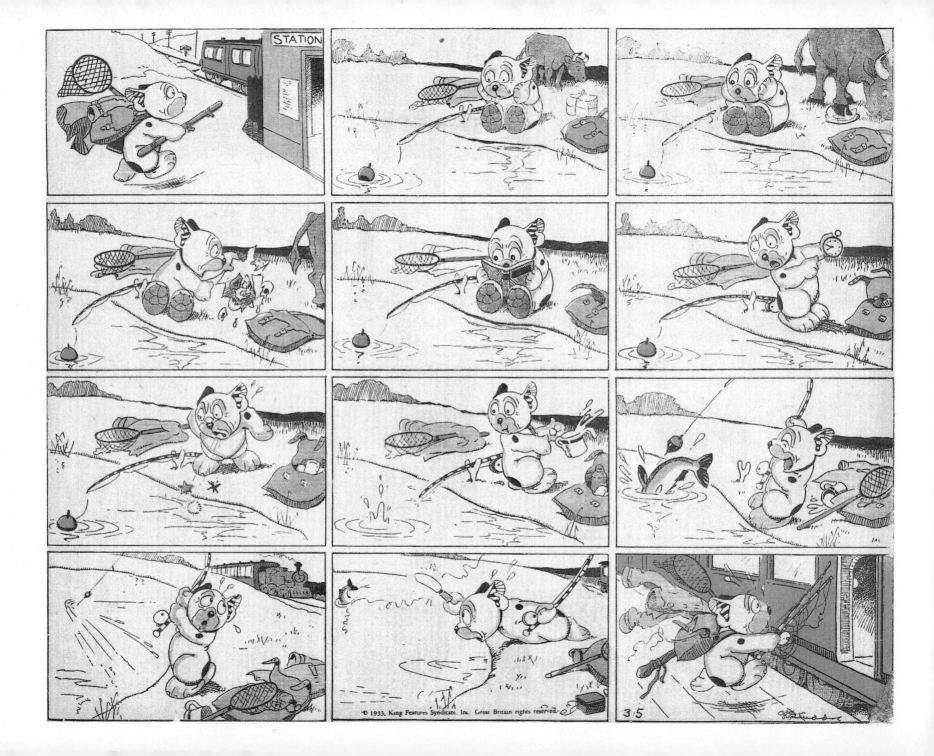

3-5

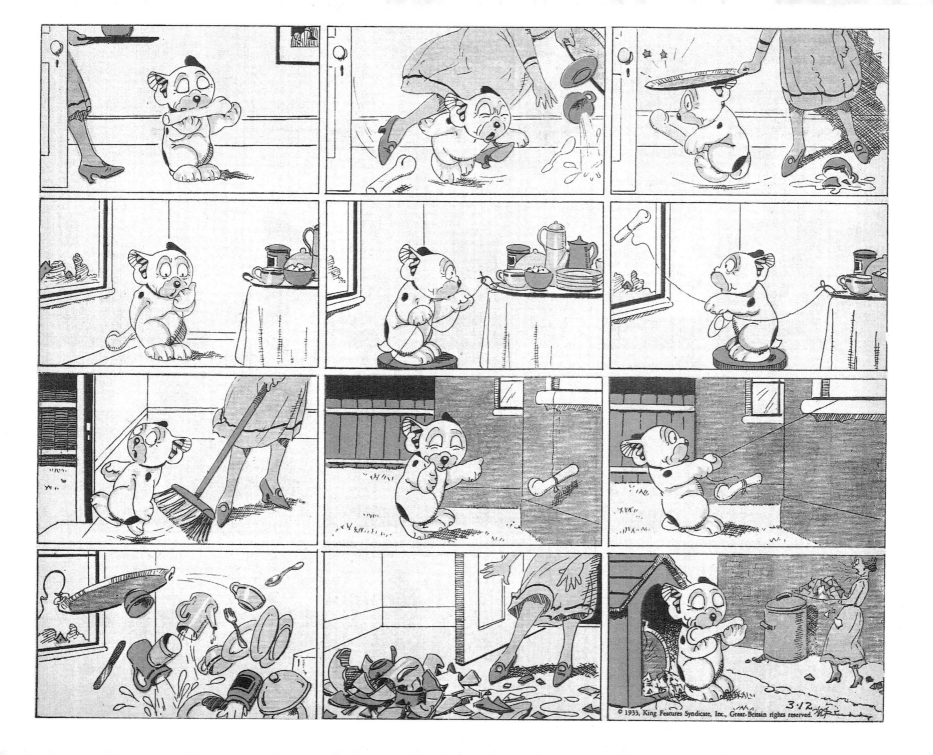

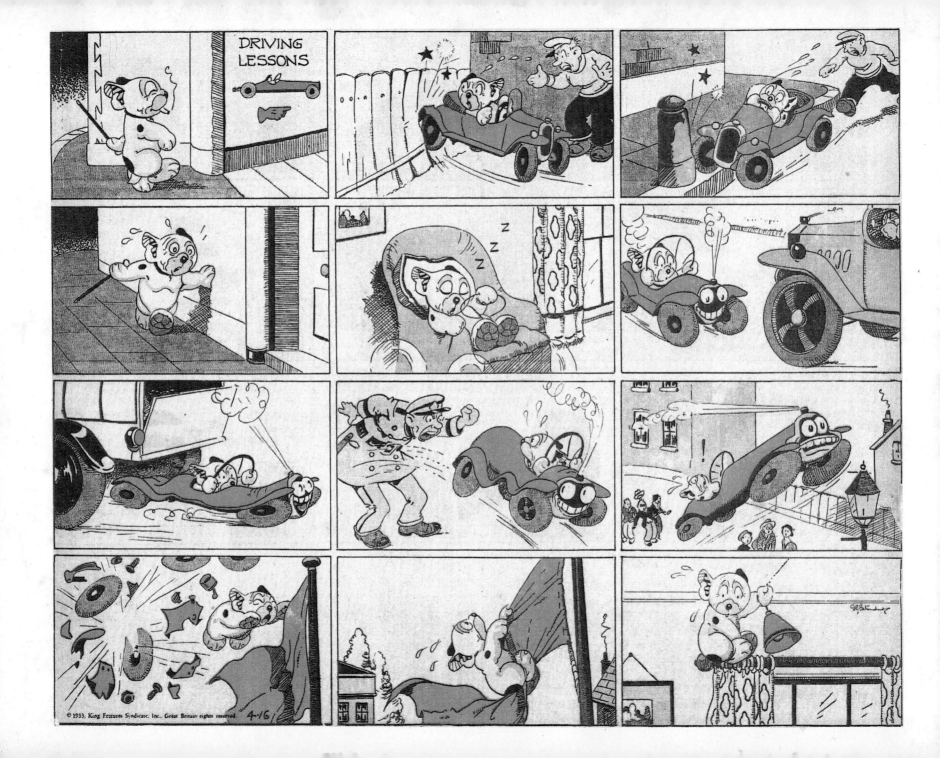